The DIAMOND EGG of WONDERS

This book is dedicated to the following, without whom none of this would be possible:
Our parents, who have always supported and encouraged us to chase our dreams.
Mimi and Esther, for motivating us every day to transform those dreams into reality.
All our readers, whose enthusiasm inspires us to continue dreaming.

The Etherington Brothers
- Adventures in Words and Pictures -
www.theetheringtonbrothers.blogspot.com

MONKEY NUTS: THE DIAMOND EGG OF WONDERS
A DAVID FICKLING BOOK 978 1 849 92169 5

First published thanks to the amazing DFC weekly comic,
May 2008 – March 2009

Published in Great Britain in 2010 by David Fickling Books,
a division of Random House Children's Publishers UK
A Random House Group Company
This edition published 2013

1 3 5 7 9 10 8 6 4 2

DAVID FICKLING BOOKS 31 Beaumont Street, Oxford, OX1 2NP

www.randomhousechildrens.co.uk
www.randomhouse.co.uk

Addresses for companies within The Random House Group Limited can be found at:
www.randomhouse.co.uk/offices.htm
THE RANDOM HOUSE GROUP Limited Reg. No. 954009
A CIP catalogue record for this book is available from the British Library.
Printed in China

The Random House Group Limited supports the Forest Stewardship Council® (FSC®), the leading international forest-
certification organisation. Our books carrying the FSC label are printed on FSC®-certified paper. FSC is the only forest-
certification scheme supported by the leading environmental organisations, including Greenpeace.
Our paper procurement policy can be found at www.randomhouse.co.uk/environment

MIX
Paper from
responsible sources
FSC
www.fsc.org
FSC® C104723

THE ETHERINGTON BROTHERS

MONKEY NUTS

The DIAMOND EGG of WONDERS

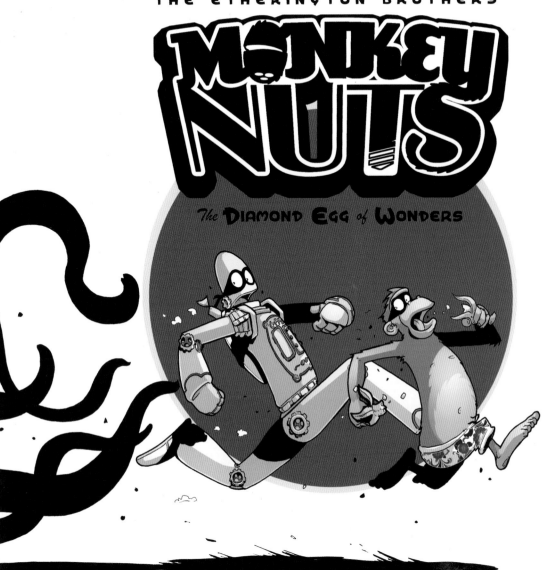

David Fickling Books

OXFORD · NEW YORK

BEEEP

BEEEP

BEEEP

MWAHAHAHAHA!

DEEP UNDERGROUND, DIRECTLY BELOW THE STRANGE AREA OF EARTH KNOWN AS **THE BERMUDA TRIANGLE,** STANDS A FORTRESS SO EVIL-LOOKING THAT IT SOMETIMES SCARES ITSELF! THIS MONSTROSITY IS CALLED **TABITHA,** AND WITHIN HER STONE NOSTRIL LIVES A BEING EVEN **MORE** EVIL THAN SHE!

CHAPTER ONE
THE TERRIBLE TERRA!

FINALLY! AFTER A LIFETIME SPENT SEARCHING EVERY CORNER OF THIS MISERABLE PLANET, I HAVE FOUND IT!

MOTHER SAID I'D FAIL! SHE CALLED ME A SILLY LITTLE VILLAIN! SHE EVEN DREW PICTURES OF ME IN **JAIL!**

BUT I HAVE PROVED THEM **ALL** WRONG! EVEN MY BROTHER, WHO STILL CALLS ME RUDE NAMES.

INSIDE

I, *LORD TERRA*, HAVE DISCOVERED THE LOCATION OF THE *DIAMOND EGG OF WONDERS!* IT IS A PRICELESS, MYSTICAL TREASURE WITH UNLIMITED POWER!

ERM, *ERIC?...*

GOOBER AN' ME WANTS TO KNOW IF WE CAN EATS DA DIAMOND EGG WHEN WE GETS IT.

YEAH ... AN' DOES IT TASTE LIKE A NORMAL EGG?

BURPLE, STOP CALLING ME ERIC! I'VE TOLD YOU A HUNDRED TIMES, I'M *LORD TERRA* NOW! ERIC IS A RUBBISH NAME FOR AN EVIL MASTERMIND!

AND NO, YOU CANNOT EAT THE EGG! IT IS WORTH MORE THAN THIS FORTRESS. NOW, PAY ATTENTION, HENCHMEN. *THIS* IS A MAP.

WHACK

AND *THIS* IS THE ISLA DE MONSTERA. THE EGG IS HIDDEN SOMEWHERE ON THIS PARADISE!

SO WHY IS WE SITTIN' HERE? LET'S FIRE UP TABITHA AND GO GETS IT!

GOOD ONE, BURPLE! NOW YOU IS FINKIN'!

NO. YOU ARE NOT.

BONK

DO YOU REMEMBER ON TUESDAY WHEN WE STOPPED OFF FOR LUNCH AT THAT LITTLE ISLAND WHERE THE NATIVES WORSHIPPED A *FOOTBALL?*

UM, YEAH.

ONE OF THE VILLAGERS I *ATE* MUST HAVE PASSED HIS SELL-BY DATE. I HAD A HORRIBLE BOUT OF FOOD POISONING WHICH BROUGHT ON -- *THE VISION!*

I SAW TWO CREATURES, TWO WARRIORS OF GOOD, WHO HAVE THE POWER TO FOIL MY SCHEME! I DID A LITTLE DRAWING OF THEM...

EARLIER TODAY I ACTIVATED TABITHA'S SONIC 'MONSTER MAGNET'. SOON EVERY LOONY AND WEIRDO IN THE AREA WILL BE DRAWN TO THIS ISLAND WITH THE SAME GOAL: TO CAUSE LOTS OF TROUBLE AND *DESTROY* THESE CHUMPS!

THE DIAMOND EGG OF WONDERS SHALL BE MINE! MWAHAHAHA!

AND SO LORD TERRA SENT HIS TERRIBLE SIGNAL PULSING UPWARDS THROUGH THE EARTH. HE REALLY IS VERY NAUGHTY.

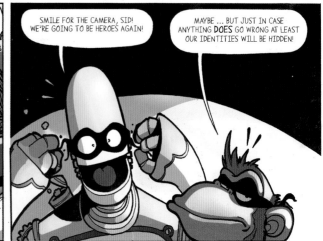

WITHIN MOMENTS THE POOR CONFUSED RESIDENTS OF CHUMP TOWN WERE ONCE MORE FLEEING FOR THEIR HAPLESS LIVES...

GRROOOOOAR!

DRIIING
DRIIING

PEOPLE ARE GOING TO SAY THIS IS MY FAULT, AREN'T THEY?

NO! EVERYONE LOVES YOU, SID! WELL ... ALMOST EVERYONE.

DOWN WITH SID!

HANG THE MONKEY!

BOO! HISS!

GO, RIVET GO!

THANK GOODNESS I'M WEARING MY MASK! C'MON, RIVET, LET'S COOL THIS FIERY FIEND DOWN A LITTLE!

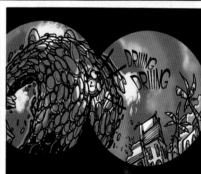
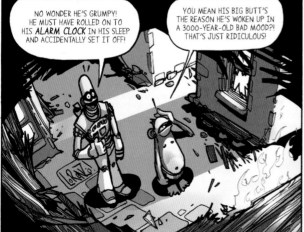

A WEEK PASSES UNEVENTFULLY AND THE MONKEY NUTS CREW DECIDE TO TAKE A WELL-DESERVED BREAK. BUT BENEATH THE STILL COASTAL WATERS DARK FORCES ARE DRAWN CLOSER UNDER LORD TERRA'S HYPNOTIC SPELL...

BEEEP BEEEP BEEEP BEEEP BEEEP

WELL BOYS, THIS IS THE LIFE!

IT CERTAINLY IS A NICE CHANGE OF PACE! NO ONE'S GOING TO TRY AND KILL US HERE!

HMMM ... I'M NOT SO SURE ABOUT THAT, RIVET.

SOMETHING PECULIAR IS GOING ON. TWO ATTACKS ON THE TOWN IN A WEEK IS ONE ATTACK TOO MANY!

NAH, THESE THINGS JUST HAPPEN, TUFT!

ARE YOU SURE ABOUT THAT, SID? IF THE CHIEF'S WORRIED, THEN I'M WORRIED!

WILL YOU BOTH RELAX! WE'RE ON HOLIDAY, AND WE'RE PERFECTLY SAFE! NOTHING CAN GO WRONG...

ABANDON HOPE ALL YE WHO FISH THESE WATERS!

EAR BEE MONSTAS

CHAPTER FOUR
go FISH!

WOAH! I THINK I'VE GOT A BITE!

SWEET BANANAS! <NGGGGGN!> IT'S A BIG ONE!

REALLY? HOW CAN YOU TELL? I CAN'T SEE A THING.

I CAN TELL, RIVET, YOU SILLY BAG OF BOLTS, BECAUSE IT'S ABOUT TO PULL ME OVERBOARD!

GRAB HOLD BOYS!

IF I'D KNOWN IT WAS GOING TO BE THIS MUCH HARD WORK I'D HAVE BROUGHT MY BIGGER ARMS!

IT'S PULLING THE BOAT! WOW! THIS FISH MUST BE A MONSTER!

HAHA ... UM, TUFT? I THINK IT'S OKAY FOR YOU TO LET GO!

LET GO? OKAY. IF YOU SAY SO.

NOT YOOOOOOU—

YANK

SPLOOOOOOSH

CHIEF? DOES THAT NORMALLY HAPPEN?

SOMETIMES. I KNEW I SHOULD HAVE HELD ON!

PLOOOOOSH

SID! THERE YOU ARE!

SO THEN CHAMP, DID YOU CATCH THAT TRICKY FISH?

ER ... NOT EXACTLY! I THINK THERE'S SOMETHING YOU SHOULD BOTH KNOW...

EXCUSE ME, GENTLEMEN. THIS IS A PRIVATE AREA. I'M AFRAID YOU'RE TRESPASSING.

OH ... POO!

WELL, WELL, WELL! THERE'S NO *TROUT* ABOUT IT, YOU *SUCKERS* ARE IN A TRICKY *PLAICE*!

PLEASE, MR DEREK, NO MORE *'FISH'* PUNS!

WHY NOT, SQUIB?!

BECAUSE THE BATTERY'S RUNNING LOW ON MY *'HORRIBLE JOKE WARNING LIGHT'*!

QUIET, RIVET! DEREK, WHAT EXACTLY IS IT THAT YOU WANT?

WELL, A WEEK AGO I WAS QUITE HAPPY JUST RULING THIS SHORELINE. BUT NOW I HAVE A NEED TO TERRORISE THE ENTIRE ISLAND AND ... *EAT THE THREE OF YOU!*

masterplan = chaos

HMMM ... SEEMS REASONABLE.

NO IT DOES *NOT*! NOT ON OUR WATCH! RIVET, IT'S *MASK TIME*!

YOU KNOW, I *NEARLY* FORGOT TO BRING THESE!

LUNCH

GRAB

DEREK THE DOOFUS! YOU ARE IN SO MUCH TROUBLE!

DROP

WHACK

RIVET! START ROWING CLOCKWISE ROUND OLD FISH FACE! FAST AS YOU CAN!

THUMP

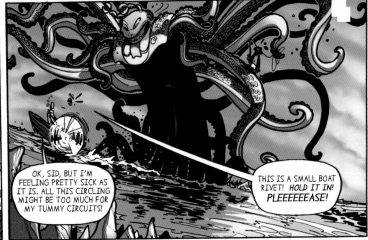

OK, SID, BUT I'M FEELING PRETTY SICK AS IT IS. ALL THIS CIRCLING MIGHT BE TOO MUCH FOR MY TUMMY CIRCUITS!

THIS IS A SMALL BOAT RIVET! HOLD IT IN! PLEEEEEEASE!

WITH THEIR HEADS FULL OF EXCITING IDEAS AND THE SEA LAPPING AT THEIR BOAT, THE GANG FAILED TO NOTICE THAT WAVES OF A FAR MORE DANGEROUS NATURE CONTINUED TO FLOW ACROSS THE ISLAND...

RETURNING FROM THEIR WELL-EARNED HOLIDAY, SID AND RIVET HEAD INTO CHUMP TOWN FOR AN IMPORTANT ERRAND. ALL APPEARS TO BE QUIET, BUT UNBEKNOWNST TO OUR HEROES, THE MONSTER MAGNET'S JUNGLE DRUMBEAT OF EVIL, ER, BEATS ON!

NOW LISTEN UP, *FEATHERS*, I REALLY DON'T SEE WHAT THE PROBLEM IS!

SHALL I EXPLAIN HOW THIS WORKS *AGAIN*, SIR?

THIS IS A **BANK**, SIR. FOLKS COME IN, OPEN ACCOUNTS AND DEPOSIT THEIR SAVINGS, SIR.

BUT THAT'S WHAT I'M *TRYING* TO DO!

THIS, SIR, IS A **BANANA**.

WELL SPOTTED! I'VE GOT *LOTS* MORE AND I'D LIKE YOU TO LOOK AFTER THEM UNTIL I'M *HUNGRY*!

WOULD YOU LIKE ME TO CALL YOU A DOCTOR, SIR? YOU SOUND LIKE A CRAZY PERSON.

3RD NATIONAL BANANA BANK OF CHUMP TOWN

CHAPTER FIVE
THE BANK RUSTLE HUSTLE!

THAT NIGHT, OUTSIDE THE 4TH NATIONAL BANK OF CHUMP TOWN...

YOU KNOW, SID, THIS JUST MIGHT BE THE GREATEST PLAN OF ALL TIME!

THANK YOU, RIVET! I'M QUITE PROUD OF IT MYSELF!

HMM ... ANOTHER VILLAIN. I AM NOW OFFICIALLY CONCERNED.

AND THIS THIEF HAS STOLEN THREE BANKS IN THE LAST THREE DAYS. HE MIGHT BE SMARTER THAN WE THINK.

NOT A CHANCE, CHIEF! THIS IS A FOOLPROOF STRATEGY!

(1) THE NUTBALL SHOWS UP AND SPOTS OUR BIG SACK OF MONEY SITTING IN THE STREET.

CHUMP

$HINY $TUFF

CA$H

TAP TAP

ROPE

(2) AS SOON AS HE GRABS THE SWAG, WE YANK ON THIS ROPE AND SNARE HIM! SIMPLE!

AW ... POO!

TUG

CA$H

BUY BANANAS

HOW CAN IT POSSIBLY FAIL?

'TIS A MERRY YARN, ME HEARTIES, BUT IT WON'T BE FOOLIN' ME!

IT'S NOT SUPPOSED TO FOOL YOU. WE'RE TRYING TO CATCH A DANGEROUS BANK ROBBER!

YAAAR, THAT BE ME! THE DREAD COWBOY, BIG BLACK BEARD!

HAHA! THAT'S A PIRATE'S NAME! COWBOYS ARE CALLED THINGS LIKE 'THE DUSTY TWIT', 'STETSON SALLY' OR 'WILD KID MALONE'!

YE SCALLYWAGS WON'T BE LAUGHIN' WHEN YE TAKE A LOOK AT YOUR BOOTY!

YOU EVEN SOUND LIKE A PIRATE! HEHE!

IT'S GONE!!

SHIVER ME TIMBERS! I'M IMPRESSED!

HAND OVER THE CASH, BEARDY! THE GAME'S UP!

NOPE. DON'T THINK I WILL. BUT I'LL TELL YE HOW I DID IT. TURNAROUND AND MEET MY PARTNER, HORSEY!

BEEEP
BEEEP
BEEEP

NICE HORSEY! NICE HORSEY! HAVE A BANANA?!

I DON'T THINK THAT'S GOING TO DO IT, SID!

I JUST HOPE YOU HAVE A BACKUP PLAN! THIS ONE APPEARS TO BE BROKEN!

I'M THINKING, I'M THINKING!

WITH SID'S MONKEY MIND HEADING FOR A MELTDOWN, AND THE MONSTER MAGNET NOW IN CONTROL OF A GIANT ROBOTIC KILLING MACHINE, EVENTS ARE ALL SET TO EXPLODE!

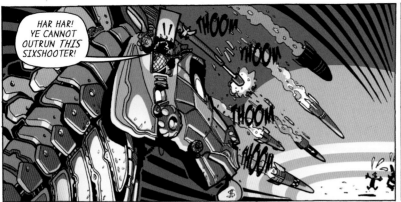

INSIDE HORSEY

THAT CHEEKY MONKEY! ACTIVATING TARGETING SYSTEMS!...

CHUNK THUNK

CLICK

BANG BOOM CROOM

I HOPE YOU'RE NEARLY READY, BOYS! I'M RUNNING OUT OF AMMO!

SID! THAT WAS MY COUSIN, JEFF, YOU JUST THREW!

HOW'S THE SCULPTING GOING, RIVET? YOU BETTER FINISH BEFORE THAT SILLY CHUMP USES ANOTHER MEMBER OF MY FAMILY AS A WEAPON!

WELL, I'M NOT VERY HAPPY WITH THE EARS BUT I GUESS SHE'LL HAVE TO DO!

WHA--?!

HEY THERE NEIGHHHHBOUR! HOW'S IT GOING?

DROP

HORSEY! WHY HAVE YE DROPPED THE BOOTY? WHY CAN'T I CONTROL YE!

OVERRIDE USER! EJECT BOSSY BLACK BEARD!

NO, HORSEY! YOU CAN'T GET RID OF ME!

BYE!

HORSEY! NO!

GOTCHA! LOOKS LIKE ALL'S FAIR IN LOVE AND WAR! HEHEHEHE!

WHOOMPH

$

WELL, BOYS, YOU'VE CAUGHT THE THIEF, CALMED THE GIANT HORSE ROBOT AND MADE THE BANKS SAFE AGAIN!

TRUE, BUT I'LL BE KEEPING MY BANANAS IN THE SAFEST PLACE OF ALL: MY BELLY!

THE BANK RUSTLING THREAT HAD BEEN VANQUISHED, BUT VICTORY LOOKED TO BE SHORT-LIVED FOR THE MONKEY NUTS TEAM. THEY NEEDED TO GET TO THE BOTTOM OF THIS CRIMEWAVE MYSTERY... ...AND FAST!

$

AND SO THE VERY NEXT DAY, DEEP IN THE HEART OF THE JUNGLE...

<PHEW!> WELL, *TUFT* CERTAINLY WASN'T LYING WHEN HE DESCRIBED THAT AS A 'BRISK STROLL'!

<GAH!> CAN'T BREATHE! CAN'T BREATHE! <AHK!>

BRISK? RIVET, I CAN HEAR MY OWN HEART STOPPING! <GAH!> I'M A LAZY MONKEY; I'M NOT BUILT FOR THIS SORT OF THING!

RELAX, SID! IT'S ALL DOWNHILL FROM HERE ...*LITERALLY!* ACCORDING TO THIS MAP, WE'VE JUST CLIMBED TO THE HIGHEST POINT ON THE ISLAND!

I STILL HAVE *NO IDEA* WHY THE CHIEF WOULD WANT US TO INVESTIGATE SUCH AN UNPOPULAR TOURIST ATTRACTION.

ME NEITHER, BUT I'M SURE OLD TUFTY HAS HIS REASONS! ONE THING I *DO* KNOW...

MAP

...THIS VIEW IS *AMAZING!*

BEEEP
BEEEP
BEEEP
BEEEP

CHAPTER SIX
TEMPER TEMPLE!

I REALLY WOULD GIVE UP IF I WERE YOU. NO ONE HAS EVER ESCAPED.

WELL, THANKS FOR THE SUPPORT, POTTYBOT, BUT I STILL THINK WE'LL GIVE IT A GO!

HMMM ... I SUPPOSE WE SHOULD START BY WORKING OUT WHAT WE KNOW ABOUT THIS PLACE.

GOOD IDEA. ER ... DO WE KNOW ANYTHING?

REMEMBER THE RHYME ABOVE THE ENTRANCE? IT ASKED FOR A DONATION OF GOLD. MAYBE THAT'S THE KEY!

IT ALSO SAID 'NO MONKEYS ALLOWED' BUT I DOUBT THAT'S OF ANY INTEREST TO YOU.

LISTEN, YOUR DEAD EMPEROR-NESS, WHAT EXACTLY HAVE YOU GOT AGAINST MONKEYS ANYWAY!

MY PET CHIMP, JOJO, POOPED IN MY CROWN ON MY 60TH BIRTHDAY. MISS THE CHEEKY CHAP NOW THOUGH. YOU REMIND ME OF HIM.

SID, MY 'COWARD' LIGHT JUST TURNED CHICKEN YELLOW! I DON'T LIKE THIS PLACE!

FEAR NOT, BUDDY! THERE CANNOT POSSIBLY BE ANYTHING DOWN HERE MORE SCARY THAN A DEAD, LOONY, MOODY GHOST.

I HEARD THAT!

OKAY, POTTY, THIS IS YOUR TEMPLE, SO WHERE'S THE SHINY STUFF? WE NEED TO MAKE AN OFFERING IF WE'RE GOING TO STOP YOUR CRAZY GUARDIAN!

SHINY STUFF? JOJO, DO YOU MEAN MY TREASURE?

<SID! HE THINKS YOU'RE HIS PET!>

BEFORE I DIED, DEAR JOJO, I ORDERED MY SLAVES TO FILL MANY, MANY GREAT ROOMS WITH ALL MANNER OF GOLDEN GOODIES.

EXCELLENT! JUST WHAT WE NEED! MASTER, ARE WE CLOSE TO ONE OF THOSE CHAMBERS?

WELL, IT'S DEFINITELY NOT IN HERE!

LET ME THINK. IT'S BEEN A WHILE BUT I'M PRETTY SURE THAT WAY RINGS A BELL.

DANGER!

SUCCESS! COME ON, RIVET, LET'S GO GRAB SOME LOOT.

YINK

CLICK

OOOPS!

OOOPS?

OR THE TUNNEL ON THE RIGHT. YES, THAT RINGS A BIGGER BELL. MY MEMORY'S NOT WHAT IT WAS.

CLUNK

AAAAAAAGH!

WEEEEEEE!

THUNK

KA-CHING

A SHORT WHILE LATER, THE GANG GATHER BELOW DECKS ON BOARD THE 'GALLEON DE MISTERIOS' - THEIR UNIQUE, SHIPWRECKED HEADQUARTERS. CHIEF TUFT HAS CALLED AN EMERGENCY MEETING...

CHAPTER SEVEN
BREAK OUT BONANZA!

OKAY, BOYS! WE'VE LOTS TO DISCUSS SO SIT UP STRAIGHT AND PAY *ATTENTION!*

SITTING CIRCUITS SET TO 'STRAIGHT' — *SIR!*

<CHOMP> <MUNCH> OKAY, SO WHAT'S THE PROBLEM, TUFTY?

THE PROBLEM, LITTLE HAIRBALL, IS THAT UNTIL THIS MORNING - WHEN YOU STOPPED THAT *WALKING STONE COFFIN* - I HAD NO IDEA WHY RANDOM WEIRDOS KEPT ATTACKING YOU *AND* CHUMP TOWN!

TUFT'S STUFF PAWS OFF!

I'D ALWAYS PRESUMED IT WAS BECAUSE THE MAYOR GAVE SID A TAP DANCING LICENCE. *<HE'S TERRIBLE!>*

I'M AN *INNOVATOR* ACTUALLY, *METAL MOUTH!* TUFT, ARE YOU SAYING YOU *DO* KNOW WHAT'S GOING ON?

WELL, I RECENTLY PICKED UP SOME STRANGE READINGS ON THE SHIP'S RADAR, SO I REWIRED RIVET'S EMERGENCY LIGHT, (*WHILE HE WAS ASLEEP*) TO PICK UP ANY *ODD* SIGNALS.

I THEN SENT YOU BOYS TO HIGHER GROUND, NEAR THAT KILLER TEMPLE, IN ORDER TO CATCH THE BEST RECEPTION, AND - *BINGO!* I MANAGED TO RECORD THIS SIGNAL!

BEEEP BEEEP BEEEP

OOOH, NICE MAP!

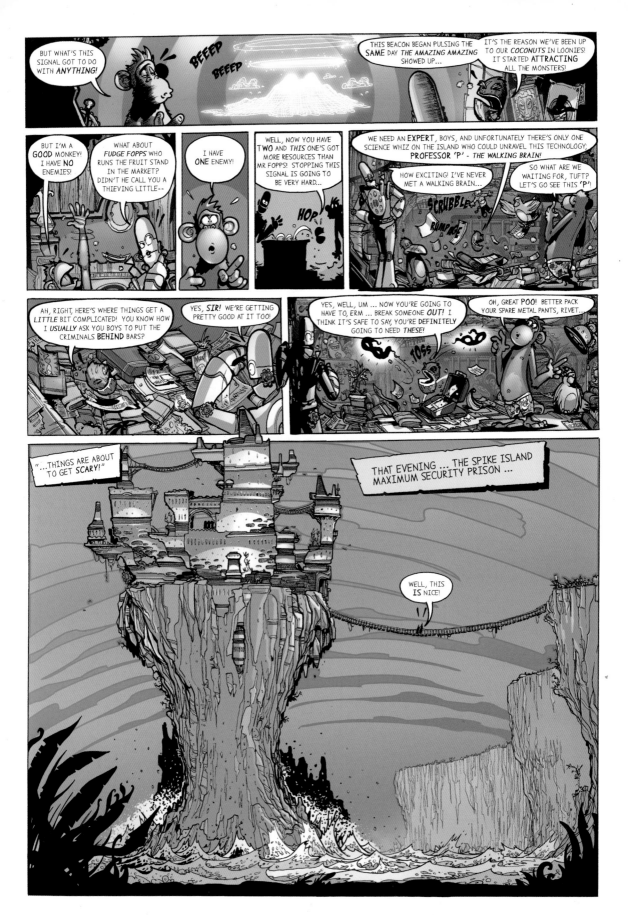

BUT WHAT'S THIS SIGNAL GOT TO DO WITH ANYTHING!

BEEEP BEEEP

THIS BEACON BEGAN PULSING THE SAME DAY THE AMAZING AMAZING SHOWED UP...

IT'S THE REASON WE'VE BEEN UP TO OUR COCONUTS IN LOONIES! IT STARTED ATTRACTING ALL THE MONSTERS!

BUT I'M A GOOD MONKEY! I HAVE NO ENEMIES!

WHAT ABOUT FUDGE FOPPS WHO RUNS THE FRUIT STAND IN THE MARKET? DIDN'T HE CALL YOU A THIEVING LITTLE--

I HAVE ONE ENEMY!

WELL, NOW YOU HAVE TWO AND THIS ONE'S GOT MORE RESOURCES THAN MR FOPPS! STOPPING THIS SIGNAL IS GOING TO BE VERY HARD...

HOP

WE NEED AN EXPERT, BOYS, AND UNFORTUNATELY THERE'S ONLY ONE SCIENCE WHIZ ON THE ISLAND WHO COULD UNRAVEL THIS TECHNOLOGY; PROFESSOR 'P' - THE WALKING BRAIN!

HOW EXCITING! I'VE NEVER MET A WALKING BRAIN...

SO WHAT ARE WE WAITING FOR, TUFT? LET'S GO SEE THIS 'P'!

SCRUBBLE RUMMAGE

AH, RIGHT, HERE'S WHERE THINGS GET A LITTLE BIT COMPLICATED! YOU KNOW HOW I USUALLY ASK YOU BOYS TO PUT THE CRIMINALS BEHIND BARS?

YES, SIR! WE'RE GETTING PRETTY GOOD AT IT TOO!

YES, WELL, UM ... NOW YOU'RE GOING TO HAVE TO, ERM ... BREAK SOMEONE OUT! I THINK IT'S SAFE TO SAY, YOU'RE DEFINITELY GOING TO NEED THESE!

TOSS

OH, GREAT POO! BETTER PACK YOUR SPARE METAL PANTS, RIVET...

"...THINGS ARE ABOUT TO GET SCARY!"

THAT EVENING ... THE SPIKE ISLAND MAXIMUM SECURITY PRISON ...

WELL, THIS IS NICE!

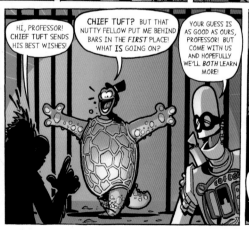

BUT OUR HEROES ONLY HAD TIME TO GRAB A COUPLE OF BANANA SANDWICHES BEFORE TUFT SENT THEM OFF WITH NEW ORDERS: THEY ARE TO FOLLOW **PROFESSOR P** INTO THE MONSTROUS INTERIOR OF THE **ISLA DE MONSTERA.** THEIR ULTIMATE DESTINATION REMAINS A MYSTERY...

BLESS MY GRAVY! **MUST** WE TRAVEL SO **FAST**?!

BUT OF COURSE, PROFESSOR! THE CHIEF ASKED US TO TEST OUT THE NEW MONKEY NUTS **CRIME-TRIKE**, AND IT WOULDN'T BE MUCH FUN IF WE WENT **SLOW**!

BRRRRM! BRRRRRM!

<GULP> OKAY, IT'S NOT FAR NOW, JUST AROUND THE NEXT BEND!

P, I'M NOT THE BRIGHTEST MONKEY IN THE CAGE, SO COULD YOU TELL ME **WHERE** WE'RE GOING?

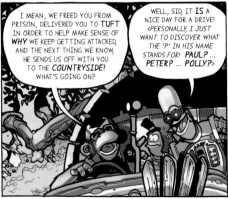

I MEAN, WE FREED YOU FROM PRISON, DELIVERED YOU TO **TUFT** IN ORDER TO HELP MAKE SENSE OF **WHY** WE KEEP GETTING ATTACKED, AND THE NEXT THING WE KNOW, HE SENDS US OFF WITH YOU TO THE **COUNTRYSIDE**! WHAT'S GOING ON?

WELL, SID, IT **IS** A NICE DAY FOR A DRIVE! <PERSONALLY, I JUST WANT TO DISCOVER WHAT THE 'P' IN HIS NAME STANDS FOR! PAUL? ... PETER? ... POLLY?>

IT STANDS FOR PEANUT, ACTUALLY. AS IN: THE SIZE OF MY HEAD. NOW YOU CAN BOTH RELAX, FOR I KNOW WHO ACTIVATED THIS TROUBLESOME **MONSTER MAGNET**, AND WHAT'S MORE I'M PRETTY SURE I CAN GUESS **WHY**!

OOOOOOOH! <IT **IS** ON THE SMALL SIDE!>

THE REASON YOU FOUND ME IN *JAIL* WAS BECAUSE OF MY CLOSE ASSOCIATION WITH THE LEGENDARY EVIL MASTERMIND: *ERIC!*

ERIC? BUT THAT'S A *RUBBISH* NAME FOR AN EVIL MASTERMIND!

YES. THAT'S WHAT EVERYONE ELSE SAID, SO HE CHANGED IT TO *LORD TERRA!* MUCH BETTER, I THINK YOU'LL AGREE.

I'VE KNOWN TERRA ALL MY LIFE. WE WENT TO SCHOOL TOGETHER. I USED TO FEED HIS GOLDFISH WHEN HE WAS ON HOLIDAY.

THAT'S JOLLY NICE OF YOU!

WELL, ASIDE FROM GOLDFISH, WE SHARED ANOTHER PASSION: *TREASURE!* LORD TERRA BECAME OBSESSED WITH ONE TREASURE IN PARTICULAR. AN ANCIENT OBJECT SAID TO POSSESS *MAGICAL* PROPERTIES!...

OOOOOOOH! <YOU KNOW, P'S ACTUALLY GOT A *TINY* HEAD WHEN YOU LOOK AT IT FROM *THIS* ANGLE!>

RIVET! ZIP IT!

<AHEM> WHICH BRINGS US *HERE!* WELCOME, GENTLEMEN... TO THE *WARP FIELD!*

HOLY ... ERM ... *HOLES IN SPACE!*

THIS COULD BE THE STRANGEST THING I'VE SEEN ... SINCE *BREAKFAST!*

REALLY?! I THOUGHT IT WOULD'VE SURPRISED THE BOLTS FROM YOUR NECK, AND THE FUR FROM YOUR FEET!

NOT ANY MORE, PROF! WE NOW LEAD *VERY* INTERESTING LIVES!

BUT I *AM* SURPRISED WE'VE NEVER HEARD OF THIS PLACE. WHAT ARE THESE ... *THINGS?*

WELL, THESE LITTLE HOLES ARE ACTUALLY ENTRANCES AND EXITS TO A *MAZE* OF SOME SORT!

THREE YEARS AGO, JUST BEFORE CHIEF TUFT IMPRISONED ME, I'D FOUND THE TREASURE LORD TERRA WAS AFTER. THEN I RAN INTO THIS FIELD!

LOOK, I'M JUST PUTTING TWO BANANAS TOGETHER HERE, BUT IS THE TREASURE INSIDE ONE OF *THESE?*

EGG

SPOT ON, YOUNG FLEABAG! CONTAINED SOMEWHERE WITHIN THE WARP MAZE IS THE MYSTICAL ... *DIAMOND EGG OF WONDERS!*

HEHEHE ... TICKLES!

PEANUT, YOU CAN'T BE SERIOUS! ALL OF OUR PROBLEMS, ALL OF THESE CRAZY LOONIES APPEARING, HAS BEEN CAUSED BY YOUR FRIEND AND HIS HUNT FOR AN EGG?!

ERM, YEP ... BUT NOT JUST ANY OLD EGG! DID I MENTION THAT IT'S DIAMOND AND FULL OF WONDERS!

YES, YOU DID. ALTHOUGH I STILL CAN'T WORK OUT WHY HE'D SEND ALL THE NASTIES AFTER US...

I BUILT THE MONSTER MAGNET AS A PRESSIE FOR LORD TERRA'S 16TH BIRTHDAY BUT I NEVER THOUGHT HE'D ACTUALLY SWITCH IT ON! MY GUESS IS HE'S USING IT AS A DISTRACTION!

AND MY BRILLIANT BRAIN IS TELLING ME THAT THE ONLY CHANCE YOU'VE GOT TO STOP TERRA IS TO REACH THIS TREASURE BEFORE HE CAN!

THAT'S GOOD ENOUGH FOR ME! COME ON, SID! WE'VE AN EGG TO CRACK AND A CASE TO SOLVE!

HOLD ON, BUDDY!

JUDGING BY OUR RECENT LUCK, THERE'S ALMOST DEFINITELY GOING TO BE SOMETHING NASTY WAITING FOR US IN THERE!

CHIMPY IS RIGHT, METAL MAN. THE LEGEND OF THE WARP WARNS OF A ROAMING RED BEAST WITH GIANT HANDS AND BLUE DUNGAREES!

WOW. THAT'S A PRETTY SPECIFIC DESCRIPTION!

ALRIGHTY THEN, YOU KNOW ME! IF THERE'S TROUBLE TO AVOID I'M FIRST IN THE QUEUE TO STAY WELL AWAY FROM--

WHUM

I AM WONKY: WEIRDO OF THE WARP AND YOU HAVE ANGERED ME! FOR EVEN DARING TO THINK ABOUT ENTERING MY MAZE WITHOUT PERMISSION, I SHALL CONFISCATE YOUR SHINY METAL FRIEND!

CRAZY KIDNAPPED COMPANIONS! THAT CRAZY JUST KIDNAPPED MY COMPANION!

HOINK

THIS WAY!

RIVET? ARE YOU OKAY? IF YOU CAN HEAR ME SEND A SIGN!

YES!

PA-TOOIE

'GRAB

'IE

TOINK

MY WORD! THAT CREATURE WAS ENORMOUS! WHAT, ON MONSTERA, ARE YOU GOING TO USE TO STOP IT?

EASY - I'VE GOT EVERYTHING I NEED RIGHT HERE PROFESSOR! EVERYTHING ... EXCEPT MY BRAVERY! NOW WHERE DID I LEAVE IT?...

GAAAAR! IF YOU WANT YOUR YELLOW TOASTER BACK, COME AND FIND IT!

UGH! SID, HIS HAND IS ALL *SWEATY!* I MIGHT *RUST!*

TRAPPED IN A WEIRD WARP MAZE WITH A GIANT MONSTER AND ALL HE'S WORRIED ABOUT IS *RUST!*...

...<SNIFF>... WHAT A *HERO!*

DON'T YOU WORRY, PAL! I'M COMING TO SAVE YOU!

BUT IT'S ALMOST CERTAIN *SUICIDE!*

I KNOW! *EXCITING,* ISN'T IT?

TERRIFYING ACTUALLY, BUT IF YOU INSIST ON FOLLOWING YOUR METAL FRIEND TO HIS DOOM, THERE'S SOMETHING YOU SHOULD KNOW...

ALL THESE HOLES ARE CONNECTED. EACH *ENTRANCE* LEADS TO A DIFFERENT *EXIT!* SEE?

NOPE, NOT REALLY. I NEVER WORRY ABOUT THE LITTLE DETAILS, PI I'M MORE OF A *'POKE-IT-AND-SEE-WHAT-HAPPENS'* SORT OF A MONKEY!

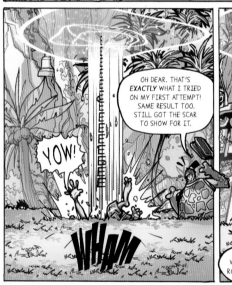

BEEEP

BEEEP

BEEEP

CHAPTER NINE
THE GREAT EGG RACE!

UM ... I'M HAVING SECOND THOUGHTS, RIVET! SHOULD WE CLIMB *BACK* INTO THE WARP HOLE?

IT IS *AWFULLY* TEMPTING, ISN'T IT!

DO YOU THINK *THAT'S* LORD TERRA?

IF IT IS, I *QUIT!* I THOUGHT MY *'WORST NIGHTMARE'* SCRAPBOOK WAS FULL, BUT I'M GOING TO ADD AN EXTRA PAGE *JUST* FOR THIS FELLA!

OH, BEFORE I FORGET, *THESE* ARE FOR YOU!

ROOT RUSTLE

WHAT ... WHERE DID YOU GET MY *SHORTS* FROM?

I *ALWAYS* CARRY A SPARE PAIR! SID, I KNOW WHAT YOU'RE LIKE - *ACCIDENTS* HAPPEN!

ERM, YES - *THANKS!* NOW, BACK TO THE MISSION. GIVE THIS THING A *PROD* AND SEE WHAT HAPPENS!

OKEY-DOKEY!

HEY! HANDS OFF TABITHA, YOU SCRAP METAL MORON!

PROD

...THE TERRIFYING...
FOAMING FALLS!

OOOOOH ... FOAMY!

WHAT'S THIS? COULD IT BE THE FABLED DIAMOND EGG? SITTING AT THE BOTTOM OF THE WATERFALL? AND IS IT... SNORING?

WOW ... THERE'S A *LOT* MORE TO THIS ISLAND THAN I EVER IMAGINED. IT'S LIKE A NEW ADVENTURE *EVERY* DAY!

UNFORTUNATELY FOR YOU TWO, *THIS* ADVENTURE WON'T HAVE A *HAPPY ENDING!*

I'VE BEEN PLANNING MY THEFT OF THE EGG FOR YEARS - BEHOLD, MY *ROBO-WALKERS!* MACHINES I CREATED JUST TO TACKLE THE FALLS, WHILE ALL *YOU* CAN DO IS WATCH! *MWAHAHAHA!*

BURPLE! GOOBER! IT'S TIME TO MOUNT UP! GO FETCH ME MY *PRIZE!* I'M OFF FOR A CUP OF TEA.

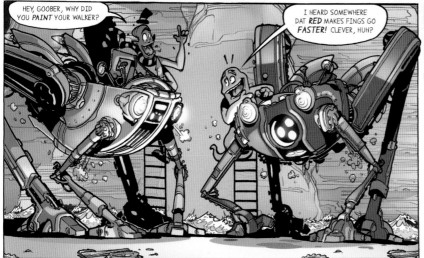

HEY, GOOBER, WHY DID YOU *PAINT* YOUR WALKER?

I HEARD SOMEWHERE DAT *RED* MAKES FINGS GO *FASTER!* CLEVER, HUH?

LORD TERRA'S *RIGHT!* THOSE MACHINES WILL CLIMB DOWN THE WATERFALL IN SECONDS! IF ONLY *WE* HAD SOMETHING LIKE THAT!

I COULDN'T AGREE MORE, BUDDY! BUT *WHERE* ARE WE GOING TO FIND SOMETHING *BETTER* THAN A MECHANICAL CLIMBING CONTRAPTION?

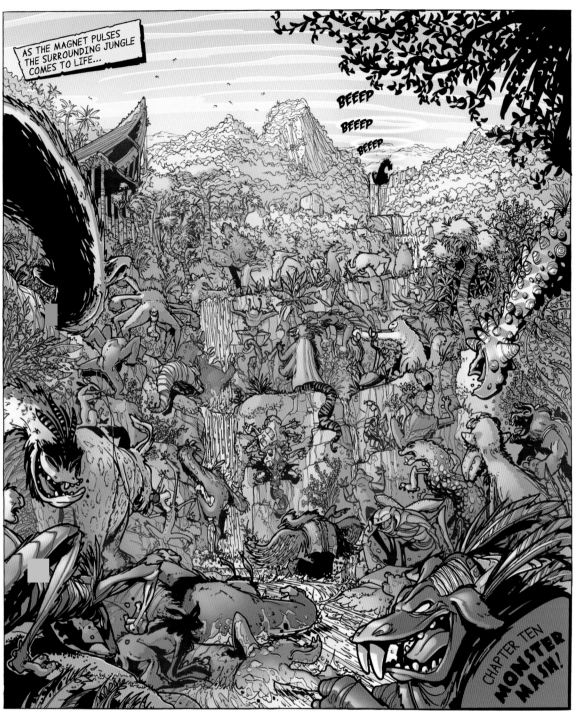

55

AND SO, IN AN ATTEMPT TO FLEE FROM THE ANGRY HORDE, LORD TERRA ACTIVATES TABITHA'S EMERGENCY LAUNCH CONTROLS. BUT ROCKETING INTO THE SKY, ESCAPE IS FAR FROM CERTAIN, AS THE FORTRESS CARRIES WITH IT A MONSTROUS CARGO...

IN THE CONTROL CENTRE OF THE FORTRESS...

S'NO GOOD, BOSS! THEY'RE EVERYWHERE! WE CAN'T EVEN **SEE** TO **STEER**!

I DON'T WANNA UPSET ANYONE BUT I FINK THEY IS **REALLY HUNGRY!** ONE OF 'EM JUST ATE THE WINDSCREEN WIPERS!

GAH! I DON'T KNOW HOW IT HAPPENED BUT IF THESE BEASTS CARRY ON LIKE THIS WE WON'T HAVE A FORTRESS **LEFT!**

THAT **MORONIC MONKEY** AND **RIDICULOUS ROBOT** MAY HAVE GOT THE BETTER OF US **THIS** TIME...

...BUT...

...I...

...PROMISE...

...YOU...

...I SHALL HAVE MY REVENGE!

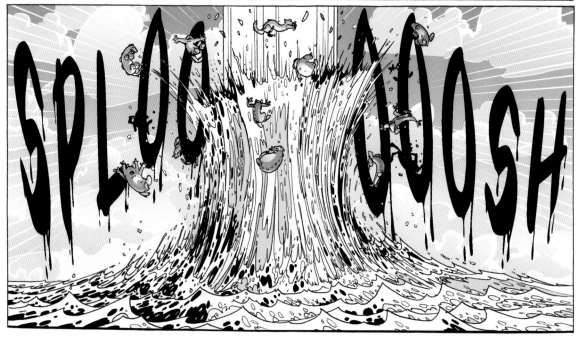

SPLOO—OOOSH

60

AT HOME WITH THE NUTS - #2
WHEN NOT FIGHTING CRIME, OUR INTREPID HEROES LIKE TO RELAX ONBOARD THEIR BASE, THE GALLEON DE MISTERIOS.

More STORIES from the DFC LIBRARY

Collect them all!